Gioacchino Rossini

2 Overtures
Il Barbiere di Siviglia / The Barber of Seville / Der Barbier von Sevilla

Edited by / Herausgegeben von
Richard Clarke

Guillaume Tell / William Tell / Wilhelm Tell

Edited by / Herausgegeben von
Lionel Salter

EULENBURG

Contents / Inhalt

Allegro vivace

EAS 116
ISBN 3-7957-6516-1
ISMN M-2002-2339-2

© 2006 Ernst Eulenburg & Co GmbH, Mainz
for Europe excluding the British Isles
Ernst Eulenburg Ltd, London
for all other countries
Edition based on Eulenburg Study Score ETP 685 and 616
CD ℗ 1989 & © 1991 Naxos Rights International Ltd

Ernst Eulenburg Ltd
48 Great Marlborough Street
London W1F 7BB

Guillaume Tell
Andante

Allegro

Andantino

Allegro vivace

Preface

Gioacchino Rossini dominated the Italian music scene and indeed the world of opera throughout the first half of the 19th century. He prepared the ground for figures such as Donizetti and even Verdi, casting a shadow over earlier opera composers including Cimarosa and Paisiello. He was born in Pesaro on 29 February 1792 to musical parents: his father was a horn player and an elected member of the Accademia Filarmonica in Bologna; his mother was a singer and teacher who performed lesser roles on the stage but nonetheless provided a family connection with the opera. Rossini learned the horn from his father and singing from Giuseppe Malerbi, a canon in Lugo, after the family had moved on from Pesaro. By 1806 Rossini was at the Liceo Musicale in Bologna where he studied cello, piano and counterpoint.

His first operatic commission dates from 1807, to set some numbers for a work called *Demetrio e Polibio*, performed some time later in 1812. *Tancredi* of 1813 was his first major success and led to those works still regularly staged: *L'Italiana in Algeri* (1813), *Il Turco in Italia* (1814), *Il Barbiere di Siviglia* (1816), *La Cenerentola* (1817) and *La Gazza Ladra* (1817). His operas up to 1823 appeared in Italy (Venice, Milan, Bologna, Naples) although it was in Paris that Rossini effectively concluded his operatic career from that point up to 1829, with *Le Comte Ory* and *Guillaume Tell*. The July Revolution of 1830, ostensibly against extraordinary taxes imposed by Charles X in France, served to annul his contract for five operas that began with *Tell* and which would have included a setting of *Faust*; with the King's reign and government over, Rossini's active presence at the forefront of music theatre likewise came to an end.

From the period of his 'retirement' after *Guillaume Tell* there are nevertheless a number of works, not least the many volumes of 'Péchés de vieillesse' (the 'sins of old age') – an often witty collection of smaller scale works (including piano pieces) in which Rossini shows that side to his character that was, as he himself said, fully prepared to set laundry lists to music. There are also works such as the more substantial *Petite Messe Solennelle* and *Stabat Mater*, as well as the duets and arias of the *Soirées Musicales*. He eventually moved to Paris again in 1855, having lived variously in Bologna and Florence during the second half of his life, and became a prominent figure in Paris society. He died on 13 November 1868 at Passy, but is buried in his native Italy in Florence, at the church of Santa Croce.

Il Barbiere di Siviglia

Composed: 1813 (as Overture to Aureliano)
First performance: (as Overture to Il Barbiere di Siviglia)
20 February 1816, Teatro Argentina, Rome
First publication: Full score, Rome, 1827
Instrumentation: 2 Flutes (2 Piccolo), 2 Oboes, 2 Clarinets, 2 Bassoons –
2 Horns, 2 Trumpets – Timpani, Bass Drum – Strings
Duration: ca. 8 minutes

Towards the end of the 19th century, Verdi expressed the view that *Il Barbiere di Siviglia* was the most beautiful *opera buffa* ever written. However its first performance on 20 February 1816 was somewhat chaotic. This seems to have been due partly to deliberate attempts to undermine Rossini by supporters of Paisiello, who had written a well-known *Barbiere* some time before; at the premiere itself there was jeering, the farcical chasing of an errant cat that had somehow invaded the stage, as well as derisive criticism from the auditorium of the composer's new gold and yellow jacket, worn especially for the event. Rossini had in fact acknowledged the elder composer's work – even giving his new opera a different title, *Almaviva, ossia L'inutil precauzione (Almaviva or The Futile Precaution)*, and had indeed written to Paisiello to express his respect for him. He had also pointed out the changes that had been made to the text in deference to Paisiello: a futile precaution indeed, it seems. The opera's popularity has, notwithstanding, remained undimmed since its first season, the second performance contrastingly having been hailed a triumph. *Il Barbiere* was Rossini's 17th stage work and broadly speaking marks the mid-point of his operatic output.

To a degree the present overture has a misleading association with the opera to which it is now linked. This music had been heard twice before: as an overture firstly to the now-obscure *Aureliano in Palmira*, premiered in December 1813, and secondly in the opera *Elisabetta, Regina d'Inghilterra* written the same year (1815) he received his contract for *Barbiere*. It is interesting that the music of this overture has links with material in the opera *Aureliano* itself, making its reuse perhaps a curious decision on Rossini's part. But considered simply as a freestanding curtain-raiser it is, in common with many of Rossini's overtures, endlessly arresting and effective.

The overture demonstrates structurally typical features of Rossini's overtures by the time he wrote the present example. A slow *maestoso* introduction, here with distinctive *balbettando* demisemiquavers for strings and bassoons, as well as a more lyrical idea for violins and flute is followed by an embryonic sonata-form 'exposition'. Two themes are presented in the *Allegro vivace*: a stealthily comical E minor theme with a martial fortissimo outburst at b48 and the G major melody at b92 with the halting, dotted-rhythms of a chromatically rising major second. This 'exposition' is concluded with one of Rossini's famous, long range *crescendi* – a build-up of tension across 36 bars in which tonic and dominant relentlessly alternate as *pianissimo* strings and *dolce* winds rise to a triumphant *fortissimo*, at which point the drama subsides into an immediate recapitulation. This idiosyncratic stamp of Rossini's musical identity first arose in his opera *L'inganno felice* premiered in 1812 and has become synonymous with the composer; it led Rossini's detractors – those in fact who supported Paisiello – to disparagingly nickname him 'Signor Crescendo'. After the recapitulation has taken its course, the *crescendo* idea is truncated at b225, losing its last 12 bars to a suddenly faster coda; it hastens the end with a precipitous descending chromatic line in the first and second violins at bb229–233 and bb242–246, pushing hard against the insistent cadence of the last 20 bars.

Guillaume Tell

Composed: 1828–9
First performance: 3 August 1829, Opéra, Paris
First publication: Full score, vocal score, Paris, 1829
Instrumentation: Piccolo, Flute, 2 Oboes (2 Cor anglais), 2 Clarinets,
2 Bassoons – 4 Horns, 2 Trumpets, 3 Trombones – Timpani, Triangle,
Cymbals, Bass Drum – Strings
Duration: ca. 12 minutes

The opera *Guillaume Tell* was Rossini's last, produced in 1829 when the composer was 37 and heralding the beginning of his well-known 40-year retirement. It was intended to be the first of five operas for the Paris Opéra; the other four had been planned to appear every other year following the premiere of *Tell* but were never destined to be written. This eventuality is explained by the July Revolution of 1830 against the increasingly unpopular government of Charles X. The contract for these operas was made under the aegis of Charles X but became void after the revolution and subsequent royal dethronement. That the composer never wrote another opera at all is perhaps attributable to fatigue on Rossini's part, after having assembled a remarkable corpus of nearly 40 operas in comparatively short time. Indeed his operatic output had slowed by this time to one opera a year, in contrast to the three or four he had written in the same time during the period before 1819.

The overture to *Guillaume Tell* falls into four distinct sections and has no real thematic connections with the music of the opera itself. It begins with an unprecedented, and wistful 'prelude' for five solo cellos with 'ripieno' cellos and basses as accompaniment, a stormy section follows in which trombones feature prominently, a contrasting pastoral fragment emerges after this with a notable solo for the cor anglais and the ubiquitous cavalry charge concludes the overture; this last section is now almost inseparable from numerous instances of discrete reuse for dramatic and even comic effect on stage and screen, which it still nevertheless demonstrates the musical strength and integrity to withstand. The windy and thunderous descending and ascending chromatics of the 'storm' section, where the woodwind and strings' maelstrom is answered by trombone hammer-blow iterations, powerfully suggests the revolutionary fervour of Tell himself and the Swiss railing against tyranny.

The Andantino at b176 features a 'ranz des vaches' ('ranks of cows') figure; this derives its contours from traditional 'alphorn' calls used by Swiss herdsmen to bring their cattle into line – those cows with bells in the lead, – a motif for which there are in fact dozens of regional variations. Beethoven's Symphony No.6 'Pastoral' contains similar suggestions of this melodic idea. It is with this 'ranz des vaches' that Schiller opens the original play on which the opera drew its libretto, where it is sung in the foreground of a typical Swiss landscape. The idea recurs after the overture, in the main opera.

For the famous *Allegro vivace* cavalry charge at b226 we find ourselves still in the grand sheltered valleys of Switzerland, with the trumpet calls ricocheting from the surrounding mountains in the echoing *stretto* horn parts. The whole passage describes musically the movement of the approaching cavalry from a far-off pianissimo, stealing upon us unexpectedly by b257, encircling us it seems in a wide arc (bb275-97) and alternately approaching and receding until the overture comes to a close, in the coda that follows a mischievous bar's pause at b430.

Although the opera was successful at its premiere, with the end of Act II being given an impromptu repeat outside the composer's house by singers and instrumentalists after the first performance, it is now rarely staged. Among Rossini's finest works, it had undergone a nine-month gestation in contrast to the two or three weeks which *Il Barbiere* is said to have taken and represents a glorious refinement of his unique style. The overture, however, remains the only part of the opera now widely known, a recognition nevertheless appropriate to its innovative details and form as well as its engaging lyricism and verve.

David Lewiston Sharpe

Vorwort

Gioacchino Rossini war während der ersten Hälfte des 19. Jahrhunderts *die* dominierende Persönlichkeit in der italienischen Musikszene und Opernwelt. Er war Wegbereiter für Komponisten wie Donizetti und sogar Verdi und stellte frühere Komponisten wie Cimarosa und Paisiello in den Schatten. Rossini wurde am 29. Februar 1792 in Pesaro als Sohn musikalischer Eltern geboren. Sein Vater war Hornist und Mitglied der *Accademia Filarmonica* in Bologna, seine Mutter Sängerin und Lehrerin. Sie spielte kleinere Bühnenrollen und stellte die Verbindung der Familie zur Oper her. Rossini lernte das Hornspiel von seinem Vater und Gesang bei Giuseppe Malerbi, einem Kanonikus in Lugo, wohin die Familie von Pesaro umgezogen war. Im Jahre 1806 wurde Rossini in das *Liceo Musicale* in Bologna aufgenommen und studierte dort Cello, Klavier und Kontrapunkt.

Rossinis erster Opernauftrag stammt aus dem Jahr 1807. Er sollte einige Musiknummern zu dem Stück *Demetrio e Polibio* schreiben, welches allerdings erst im Jahr 1812 aufgeführt wurde. *Tancredi* aus dem Jahr 1813 war dann sein erster großer Erfolg und führte schließlich zu den heute noch regelmäßig aufgeführten Werken wie *L'Italiana in Algeri* (1813), *Il Turco in Italia* (1814), *Il Barbiere di Siviglia* (1816), *La Cenerentola* (1817) und *La Gazza Ladra* (1817). Die bis 1823 komponierten Opern erschienen auf den Bühnen Italiens (Venedig, Mailand, Bologna und Neapel); Rossini beschloss seine Karriere als Opernkomponist jedoch von jenem Jahr an bis 1829 mit *Le Comte Ory* und *Guillaume Tell* in Paris. Die Julirevolution von 1830, die sich angeblich gegen die von Charles X. eingeführten außergewöhnlichen Steuern richtete, nutzte man dazu, den mit Rossini geschlossenen Vertrag über fünf Opern aufzulösen. Diese Auftragsserie begann mit *Guillaume Tell* und hätte eine Vertonung des Faust enthalten. Mit dem Ende der Herrschaft des Königs war auch Rossinis Präsenz an der Spitze der Musiktheaterszene beendet.

In der Zeit von Rossinis „Ruhestand" – nach der Entstehung des *Guillaume Tell* – sind trotzdem viele Werke entstanden. Dazu zählen die zahlreichen Bände der *Péchés de vieillesse* („Alterssünden"), eine oft geistreich-witzige Sammlung kleinerer Werke, darunter Klavierstücke, in denen Rossini zeigt, dass er, wie er es selbst einmal ausdrückte, in der Lage war, sogar Wäschelisten zu vertonen. Unter den Werken aus dieser Zeit befinden sich durchaus auch bedeutendere wie die *Petite Messe Solennelle*, das *Stabat Mater* sowie die Duette und Arien, die unter dem Titel *Soirées Musicales* veröffentlicht worden sind. Nachdem Rossini während seiner zweiten Lebenshälfte in Bologna und Florenz gelebt hatte, zog er schließlich im Jahr 1855 wieder nach Paris und war dort eine bedeutende Persönlichkeit der Pariser Gesellschaft. Er starb am 13. November 1868 in Passy (damals noch ein Vorort von Paris), wurde jedoch im heimatlichen Italien in der Kirche *Santa Croce* in Florenz beigesetzt.

Il Barbiere di Siviglia

Komponiert: 1813 (als Ouvertüre zu Aureliano)
Uraufführung: (als Ouvertüre zu Il Barbiere di Siviglia)
20. Februar 1816, Teatro Argentina, Rom
Erstveröffentlichung: Partitur, 1827, Rom
Besetzung: 2 Flöten (2. auch Piccolo), 2 Oboen, 2 Klarinetten, 2 Fagotte –
2 Hörner, 2 Trompeten – Pauken, Große Trommel – Streicher
Dauer: etwa 8 Minuten

Ende des 19. Jahrhunderts brachte Verdi die Meinung zum Ausdruck, dass *Il Barbiere di Siviglia* die schönste Opera buffa sei, die je geschrieben wurde. Die Uraufführung am 20. Februar 1816 verlief jedoch ein wenig chaotisch. Dies scheint teilweise auf absichtliche Versuche der Anhänger Paisiellos zurückzugehen, die Rossinis Arbeit unterminieren wollten. Paisiello hatte nämlich einige Zeit zuvor eine allgemein bekannte Vertonung des *Barbiere di Siviglia* komponiert. Während der Uraufführung von Rossinis Oper johlte das Publikum, eine Katze, die irgendwie auf die Bühne gelangt war, wurde gejagt und Rossinis neue goldgelbe Jacke, die er extra zu diesem Anlass trug, wurde vom Publikum höhnisch kritisiert. Rossini hatte das Werk des älteren Komponisten jedoch respektiert und gab seiner neuen Oper sogar einen anderen Titel: *Almaviva, ossia L'inutil precauzione* („Almaviva oder Die vergebliche Vorsichtsmaßnahme"). Auch hatte er Paisiello geschrieben, um ihm Respekt zu zollen und auf die Textänderungen hinzuweisen, die er aus diesem Grund vorgenommen hatte – in der Tat eine „vergebliche Vorsichtsmaßnahme", wie es scheint. Ungeachtet dessen blieb der Erfolg von Rossinis Oper seit jener Saison ungetrübt, denn die zweite Aufführung war im Gegensatz zur ersten ein großer Erfolg. *Il Barbiere di Siviglia* war Rossinis 17. Bühnenwerk und markiert den Mittelpunkt seines Opernschaffens.

In gewissem Maße steht die vorliegende Ouvertüre in einem irreführenden Zusammenhang mit der Oper, mit der sie jetzt verbunden ist. Die Musik wurde zuvor schon zweimal verwendet: zuerst als Ouvertüre zu dem verschollenen Werk *Aureliano in Palmira*, uraufgeführt im Dezember 1813, und dann zu der Oper *Elisabetta, Regina d'Inghilterra* aus dem Jahr 1815, die im selben Jahr komponiert wurde, in dem Rossini seinen Vertrag für *Il Barbiere di Siviglia* erhielt. Interessant ist, dass die Musik dieser Ouvertüre Material aus der Oper *Aureliano* enthält. Somit erscheint die Wiederverwendung der Ouvertüre etwas merkwürdig. Betrachtet man sie jedoch einfach nur als allein stehendes kurzes Vorspiel, so ist sie, genauso wie viele andere Ouvertüren Rossinis, unglaublich faszinierend und wirkungsvoll.

Die Ouvertüre weist strukturell typische Merkmale von Rossinis Ouvertüren aus dieser Zeit auf. Der langsamen Einleitung (*maestoso*) mit den charakteristischen Zweiunddreißigstelnoten (*balbettando*) in den Streichern und Fagotten und dem eher lyrischen Motiv in den Violinen und Flöten folgt der Keim einer Sonatenform-Exposition. Im *Allegro vivace* werden zwei Themen vorgestellt: ein verstohlen-komisches Thema in e-Moll mit einem martialischen

Fortissimo-Ausbruch in Takt 48 und die G-Dur-Melodie in Takt 92 mit dem zögernden punktierten Rhythmus in chromatisch aufsteigenden großen Sekunden. Diese „Exposition" endet mit einem von Rossinis berühmten lang andauernden Crescendi. Die Spannungskurve, in der Tonika und Dominante unaufhörlich in den Streichern (*pianissimo*) und Bläsern (*dolce*) alternieren, steigt über 36 Takte hinweg bis zum triumphierenden Fortissimo. An diesem Punkt lässt die Dramatik etwas nach und es geht unmittelbar in die Reprise über. Dieser für Rossini so typische Aufbau erschien zum ersten Mal in seiner Oper *L'inganno felice*, die 1812 uraufgeführt wurde, und wurde schließlich mit dem Komponisten gleichgesetzt. Dies brachte Rossinis Kritiker – die Anhänger Paisiellos – dazu, ihn geringschätzig als „Signor Crescendo" zu bezeichnen. Nachdem die Reprise durchlaufen ist, wird das Crescendo in Takt 225 abgebrochen und verliert die letzten zwölf Takte zugunsten einer plötzlich schnelleren Coda. Sie beschleunigt den Schluss mit einer sich überschlagenden chromatischen Abwärtslinie in den ersten und zweiten Violinen (T. 229–233 und T. 242–246) und setzt sich stark gegen die beharrliche Kadenz in den letzten 20 Takten durch.

Guillaume Tell

Komponiert: 1828–1829
Uraufführung: 3. August 1829, Opéra de Paris
Erstveröffentlichung: Partitur und Klavierauszug, 1829, Paris
Besetzung: Piccolo, Flöte, 2 Oboen (2. auch Englischhorn), 2 Klarinetten,
2 Fagotte – 4 Hörner, 2 Trompeten, 3 Posaunen – Pauken, Triangel,
Becken, Große Trommel – Streicher
Dauer: etwa 12 Minuten

Guillaume Tell ist die letzte Oper, die Rossini komponiert hat. Sie entstand 1829, als der Komponist 37 Jahre alt war, und leitete Rossinis berühmten „Ruhestand" im Alter von nur 40 Jahren ein. Die Oper sollte ursprünglich die erste von fünf Produktionen für die Pariser Oper werden. Die anderen vier waren für jedes weitere Jahr nach der Premiere von *Guillaume Tell* geplant, sollten aber letztendlich nie geschrieben werden. Dies erklärt sich durch die Julirevolution von 1830, die sich gegen die zunehmend unbeliebte Regierung Charles X. richtete. Der Vertrag für diese Opern, der noch unter Charles X. zustande gekommen war, wurde nach der Revolution und der sich anschließenden Entthronung des Königs ungültig. Dass der Komponist danach nie wieder eine Oper komponiert hat, ist vielleicht auch durch eine gewisse Müdigkeit Rossinis zu erklären, der innerhalb einer relativ kurzen Zeitspanne eine bemerkenswerte Sammlung von 40 Opern komponiert hatte. Allerdings hatte sich seine Produktion zu jener Zeit schon auf eine Oper pro Jahr verlangsamt, nachdem er in der Zeit vor 1819 drei oder vier Opern pro Jahr geschrieben hatte.

Die Ouvertüre zu *Guillaume Tell* besteht aus vier verschiedenen Abschnitten und hat keine wirklich thematische Verbindung zu der Musik der eigentlichen Oper. Sie beginnt mit einem beispiellosen, wehmütigen „Vorspiel" für fünf Solo-Celli, begleitet von den Tutti-Celli und den Kontrabässen. Es folgt ein stürmischer Abschnitt, in dem die Posaunen besonders hervortreten. Im Gegensatz dazu erscheint daraufhin das Fragment einer Pastorale mit einem bemerkenswerten Solo für Englischhorn. Die Ouvertüre endet dann mit der so genannten „Reiterattacke". Dieser letzte Abschnitt ist heute fast untrennbar von den zahlreichen Beispielen, in denen diese Musik eigenständig für dramatische und sogar komische Effekte auf der Bühne und im Film wieder verwendet wurde, hält dem aber durch seine musikalische Kraft und Unbestechlichkeit stand. Die windige und donnernde auf- und absteigende Chromatik der „Sturm-Passage", in der der Strudel der Holzbläser und Streicher von den Posaunen mit hämmernden Wiederholungen beantwortet wird, vermittelt kraftvoll die revolutionäre Leidenschaft Wilhelm Tells und der Schweizer, mit der sie gegen die Tyrannei wettern.

Das *Andantino* in Takt 176 enthält einen so genannten „ranz des vaches" (Kuhreigen). Dieses Motiv ist von den traditionellen Alphorn-Rufen abgeleitet, mit denen die Schweizer Hirten ihre Rinder in eine Reihe brachten – die Kühe mit den Glocken allen voran. Für dieses Motiv gibt es in der Tat dutzende regionale Variationen. Beethovens 6. Symphonie („Pastorale") enthält ähnliche Anklänge an diese Melodie. Mit eben diesem „ranz des vaches" eröffnet auch Schiller das originale Theaterstück, auf das sich das Libretto stützt. Er wird dort vor einer typisch schweizerischen Landschaft gesungen. Das Motiv taucht nach der Ouvertüre in der Oper wieder auf.

Bei der berühmten „Reiterattacke" im *Allegro vivace* in Takt 226 befinden wir uns immer noch in den behüteten schweizerischen Tälern; die Trompetenrufe prallen von den umliegenden Bergen ab und spiegeln sich in den Hornstimmen wider. Der gesamte Abschnitt beschreibt musikalisch die Bewegung der herannahenden Kavallerie. Von einem weit entfernten Pianissimo ausgehend, schleicht sie sich in Takt 257 unerwartet an uns heran. Es scheint, als ob sie uns in einem weiten Bogen einkreisen (T. 275–297) und sich abwechselnd annähern und entfernen würde, bis die Ouvertüre schließlich nach einem schelmischen Pausentakt (Takt 430) mit der Coda zum Schluss kommt.

Obwohl die Uraufführung der Oper ein großer Erfolg war und der Schluss des zweiten Aktes von den Sängern und Instrumentalisten nach der Uraufführung spontan vor Rossinis Haus wiederholt wurde, wird sie heute nur selten aufgeführt. *Guillaume Tell* zählt zu Rossinis besten Werken. Er beschäftigte sich neun Monate lang mit der Komposition – ganz im Gegensatz zu der Oper *Il Barbiere di Siviglia*, von der behauptet wird, sie sei in nur zwei bis drei Wochen komponiert worden – und stellt eine wunderbare Weiterentwicklung seines einzigartigen Stils dar. Die Ouvertüre ist heute allerdings der einzige Teil der Oper, der einem breiten Publikum bekannt ist – eine Anerkennung nichtsdestotrotz, die den einfallsreichen Details, der Form sowie der bezaubernden Lyrik der Komposition gerecht wird.

David Lewiston Sharpe
Übersetzung: Uta Heipp

Il Barbiere di Siviglia
Sinfonia

Gioacchino Rossini
(1792–1868)

I. Andante maestoso

3

4

6

14

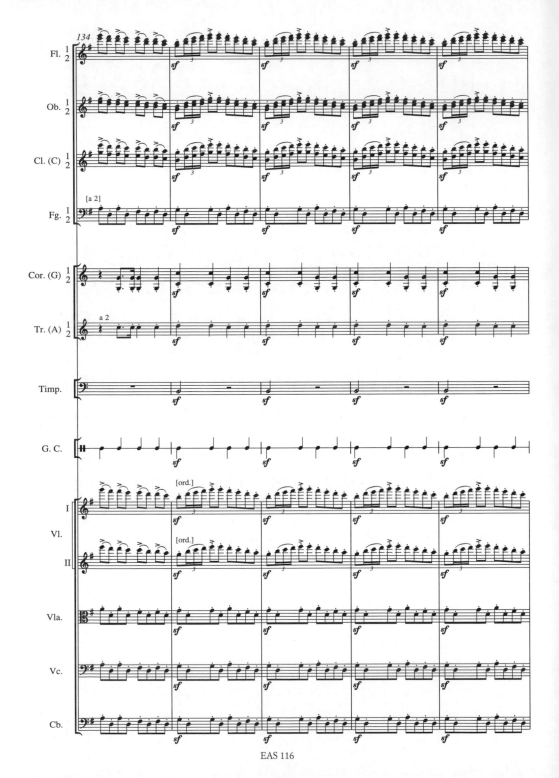

24

26

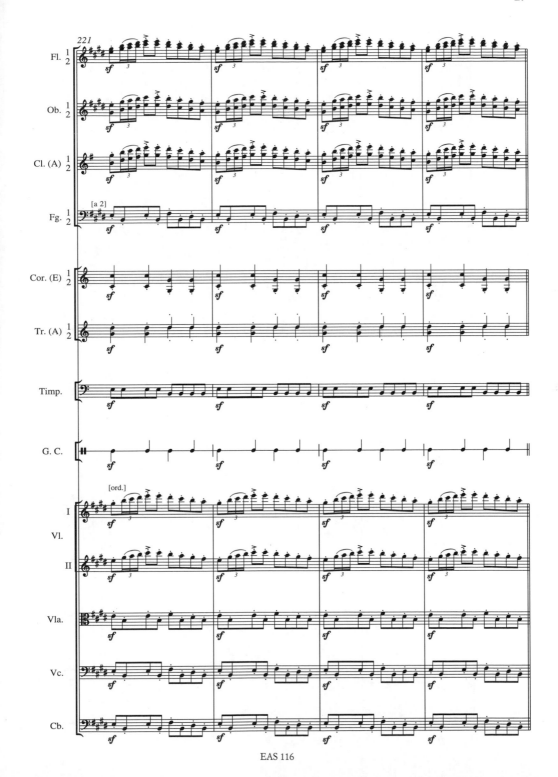

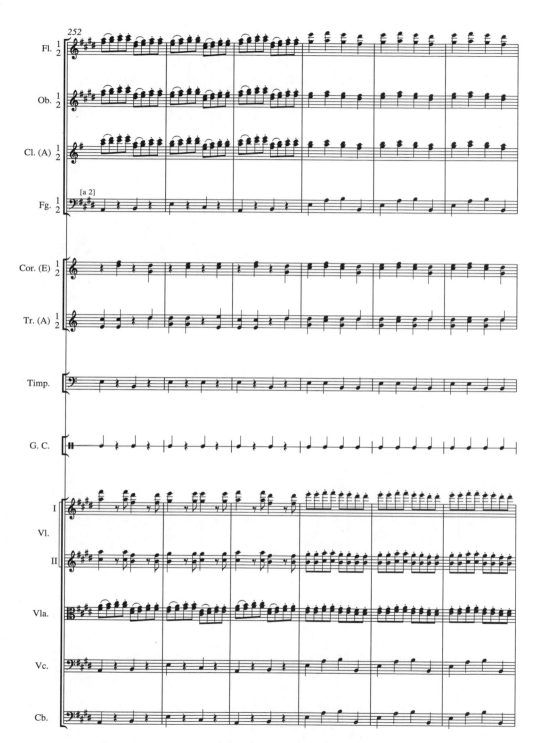

Guillaume Tell
Overture

Gioacchino Rossini
(1792–1868)

I. Andante (♩ = 54)

Piccolo

Flauto

Oboe 1 2
(anche Corno inglese)

Clarinetto (A) 1 2

Fagotto 1 2

(G) 1 2
Corno
(E) 3 4

Tromba 1 2

Trombone 1 2
3

Timpani (E, B)

Triangolo

Piatti e
Gran Cassa

Violino I

Violino II

Viola

Violoncelli Soli 1
2
3
4
5

Violoncelli
ripieni

Contrabbasso

EAS 116

© 2006 Ernst Eulenburg Ltd, London
and Ernst Eulenburg & Co GmbH, Mainz

40

44

50

60

64